£6.50

Optional Piano Accompaniment a~

Winners
Galore for Descant Recorder

PETER LAWRANCE

This collection is for players, of all ages, to dip into and enjoy.

Eine Sammlung für alle, die musizieren, für Jung und Alt, für Entdecker und Liebhaber.

Tous les musiciens, quelque soit leur âge, trouveront plaisir à feuilleter ce recueil de morceaux choisis.

ACKNOWLEDGEMENT

We should like to thank Marion Scott for her contribution in the preparation of this publication. Marion Scott teaches at the Kent Music School and is Professor of Recorder at the Guildhall School of Music and Drama Junior Dept and at Trinity College of Music.

Fingering Chart for Descant Recorder

○ OPEN HOLE   ● CLOSED HOLE   ◐ SLIGHTLY OPEN THUMB HOLE

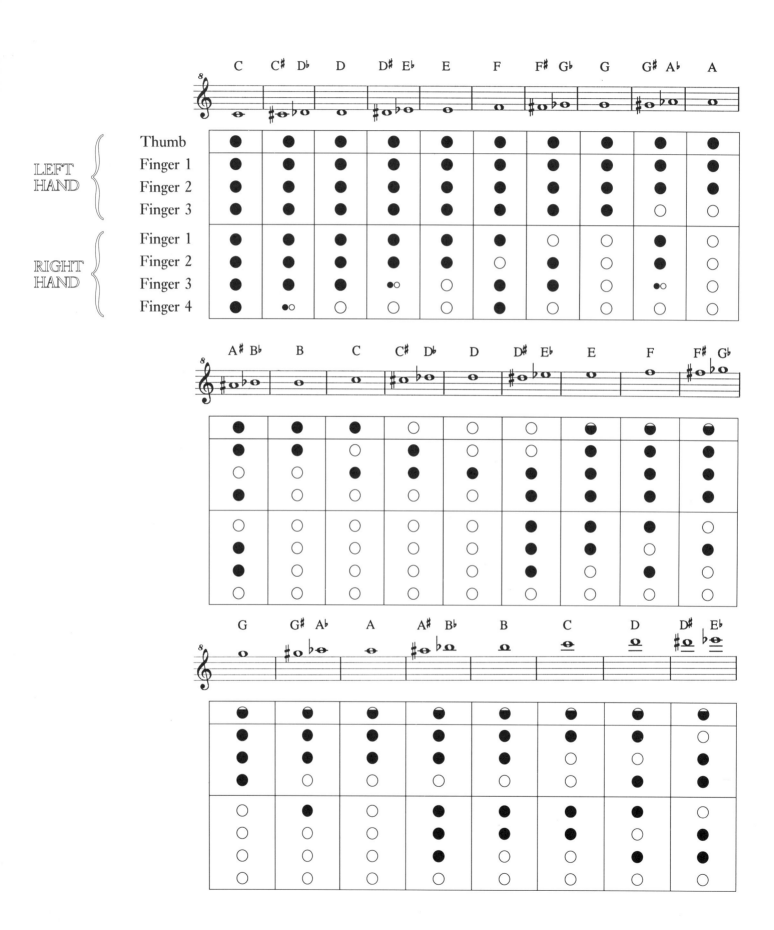

Memory Joggers

TIME VALUES

	AMERICAN NAMES						
1 SEMIBREVE	whole note	𝅝				―	semibreve rest
2 MINIMS	half notes	𝅗𝅥	𝅗𝅥			▬	minim rest
4 CROTCHETS	quarter notes	♩	♩	♩	♩	𝄽	crotchet rest
8 QUAVERS	eighth notes	♪ ♪ ♪ ♪ ♪ ♪ 𝅘𝅥𝅮𝅘𝅥𝅮				𝄾	quaver rest
16 SEMIQUAVERS	sixteenth notes	𝅘𝅥𝅯𝅘𝅥𝅯𝅘𝅥𝅯𝅘𝅥𝅯𝅘𝅥𝅯𝅘𝅥𝅯𝅘𝅥𝅯𝅘𝅥𝅯𝅘𝅥𝅯𝅘𝅥𝅯𝅘𝅥𝅯𝅘𝅥𝅯				𝄿	semiquaver rest

A dot after a note means hold the note for half as long again   𝅗𝅥. = 𝅗𝅥 + ♩

TIME SIGNATURES

The top number tells you how many beats to count in each bar

The bottom number tells you what kind of note is used for the beat

$\dfrac{2}{4}$ = $\dfrac{2}{♩}$ beats in a bar

$\dfrac{3}{4}$ = $\dfrac{3}{♩}$ beats in a bar

$\dfrac{4}{4}$ = $\dfrac{4}{♩}$ beats in a bar

$\dfrac{6}{8}$ = $\dfrac{6}{♪}$ in a bar, or 2 𝅘𝅥𝅭. beats

TEMPO

♩ = 120 means 120 ♩ beats in a minute

♩. = 90 means 90 ♩. beats in a minute

Foreign words used for performance directions

Adagio	slowly
Allegro	quick
Andante	at a walking pace
Brio	vigour
Con	with
Espressione	feeling
Marziale	like a march
Moderato	at a medium speed
Rall	short for rallentando ...... gradually getting slower
Rit	short for ritardando ...... gradually getting slower
a tempo	back to the first speed

Signs

𝄐	Pause
D.C. al Fine	go back to the beginning, end at Fine
D.S. al Fine	go back to the sign 𝄋 and end at Fine
𝄆 repeat these bars 𝄇	

Dynamics

p	soft
mp	moderately soft
mf	moderately loud
f	loud
<	crescendo ...... gradually louder
>	decrescendo ...... gradually softer

Playing reminders

Tonguing	Use 'te' for short, lively notes but use 'du' for gentle, longer notes
✓	Breath mark
(slur)	Slur - tongue the first note and keep blowing (without tonguing) onto the next note
(staccato)	Staccato - very short and sharp - use 'te'
(accent)	Accent - tongue hard

Happy Birthday

MILDRED HILL/PATTY HILL

Wombling Song

MIKE BATT

Theme from Ninth Symphony

BEETHOVEN

Bridal March

WAGNER

© 1994 Brass Wind Publications

Birdie Song

TERRY RENDALL/WERNER THOMAS

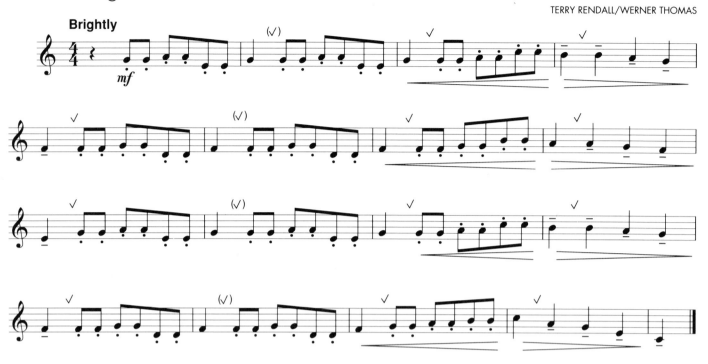

Dance of the Cuckoos Laurel and Hardy Theme

T. MARTIN HARVEY

We Wish You a Merry Christmas

TRADITIONAL WEST COUNTRY

© 1994 Brass Wind Publications

Postman Pat

BRYAN DALY

Can-can from 'Orpheus in the Underworld'

OFFENBACH

Theme from 'William Tell'

ROSSINI

Give Me Joy in My Heart

TRADITIONAL

© 1994 Brass Wind Publications

Barwick Green The Archer's Theme

ARTHUR WOOD

Nessun Dorma

PUCCINI

Tie Me Kangaroo Down, Sport

ROLF HARRIS

In Dulci Jubilo

TRADITIONAL CAROL

Miss Marple Theme

KEN HOWARD/ALAN BLAIKLEY

Morning from 'Peer Gynt'

GRIEG

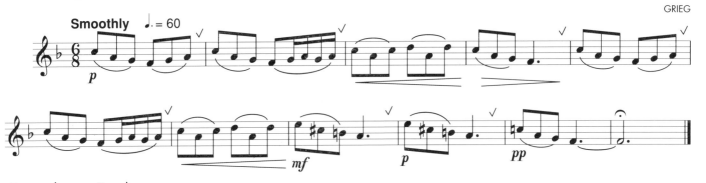

Drunken Sailor

ENGLISH DRINKING SONG

© 1994 Brass Wind Publications

Eyelevel Van der Valk Theme

JACK TROMBEY

Portsmouth

OLD ENGLISH AIR

Prelude from 'L'Arlésienne'

BIZET

Kalinka

RUSSIAN

Flintstones Theme

WILLIAM HANNA

Fawlty Towers Theme

DENNIS WILSON

Linden Lea

VAUGHAN WILLIAMS

Land of Hope and Glory

ELGAR

Last of the Summer Wine

RONNIE HAZLEHURST

Liberty Bell   Monty Python Theme

SOUSA

Blackadder Theme

HOWARD GOODALL

Emmerdale Farm Theme

TONY HATCH

© 1994 Brass Wind Publications

Aria from 'The Marriage of Figaro'

MOZART

I Could Be So Good For You Minder Theme

PATRICIA WATERMAN/GERARD KENNY

Teddy Bears Picnic

BRATTON/KENNEDY

© 1994 Brass Wind Publications

In The Mood

ANDY RAZAF/JOE GARLAND

Spread a Little Happiness

VIVIAN ELLIS/CLIFFORD GREY

Muppet Show Opening

JIM HENSEN/SAM POTTLE

Bolero

RAVEL

The Entertainer   'The Sting' Theme

SCOTT JOPLIN